The Three Little Pigs

Retold and Illustrated by Dr. Stacey Zlotnick

drstaceyzlotnick@gmail.com

1st Edition: 2019

Publisher's Cataloging-in-Publication Data:

Names: Zlotnick, Dr. Stacey A, author and illustrator.

Title: The Three Little Pigs: An Imaginative Decision Tree Production / Dr. Stacey A Zlotnick.

Series: Two-Side Tails

Description: La Jolla, California: Dr. Stacey Zlotnick, 2019.

Summary: Retelling of the classic tale, Three Little Pigs, told in the perspective of the wolf.

Identifiers: LCCN 2019920533 ; ISBN 978-1-7344164-2-8 (ebook)
ISBN: 978-1-7344164-0-4 (paperback); 978-1-7344164-0-4 (hardcover)

Author's Message

"We are all doing the best we can."
– Dr. Stacey Zlotnick

Dear Kayla,
always follow
your heart.
♡ Dr. Stacy

Once upon a time a momma pig sent her three little piglets into the world.

"It is time for you to explore the world," she said.

She gave them 5 dollars each, a hug, and a message. "Always do your best and follow your heart, and remember, I am always with you. I love you."

5

The first Adventurous Little Pig met a man selling straw.
He got an idea.
"I know. I can build a house out of straw" he told himself.
And he handed over his 5 dollars and proudly started building
his house.

7

The second Industrious Little Pig met a man selling stones. He got an idea.
"I know. I can build a house out of stones," he said to himself and he handed over his 5 dollars and started build-ing his house.

He spent all day and night planning out the details of his house to make it perfect.

Now the third Creative Pig did something different.
He kept his 5 dollars and asked his friends from all over the
world to send him some things. He asked for flags, art and
statues!

Now, once upon a time there was a wolf who got separated from his family.
He went wandering into the woods to find some friends and got lost.
The more he tried to find them, the more lost he became.
He didn't know what to do.

The scared and hungry wolf became hopeful when he came across a pig in a straw house.
He yelled in a deep voice,
"Little pig, little pig, let me in."
The Adventurous Pig replied, "No! Not by the hair of my chinny, chin, chin."

13

The scared wolf said,
"Then I'll **huff** and I'll **puff** and I will blow your house in."
The Adventurous Pig bravely repled,
"Go right ahead. I am not leaving!"

15

The wolf didn't get his way, so he **huffed** and he **puffed** away from the house- singing a song.

The angry and hungry wolf then came across a pig in a
meticulous house.
He yelled in a deep voice,
"Little pig, little pig, let me in."
The Industrious Pig was confused,
"This doesn't make sense," he said.
"He does not have an appointment."

Let me in!

Where is his appointment?

The frustrated wolf said,
"Then I'll **huff** and I'll **puff** and I will blow your house in."
And the Industrious Pig replied matter of factly,
"Apologies Mr. Wolf, I can not let you in. If you want to
come inside, you must schedule a time."

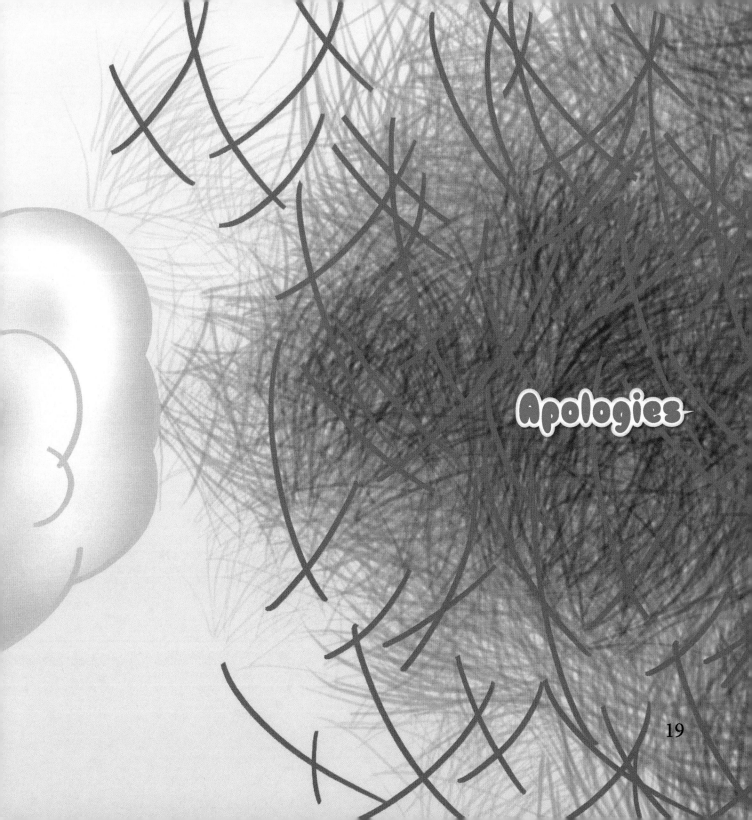

Apologies

19

The wolf didn't get his way, so he **huffed** and he **puffed** away from the house- singing a song.

The angry and tired wolf came across the third house.
He yelled in a deep voice,
"Little pig, little pig, let me in."
The Creative Pig replied, "Oh! Did you bring me a flag?
Why did you come?"

"I am here to find a different way,"
said the wolf.

WHAT WAY
DOES HE CHOOSE...

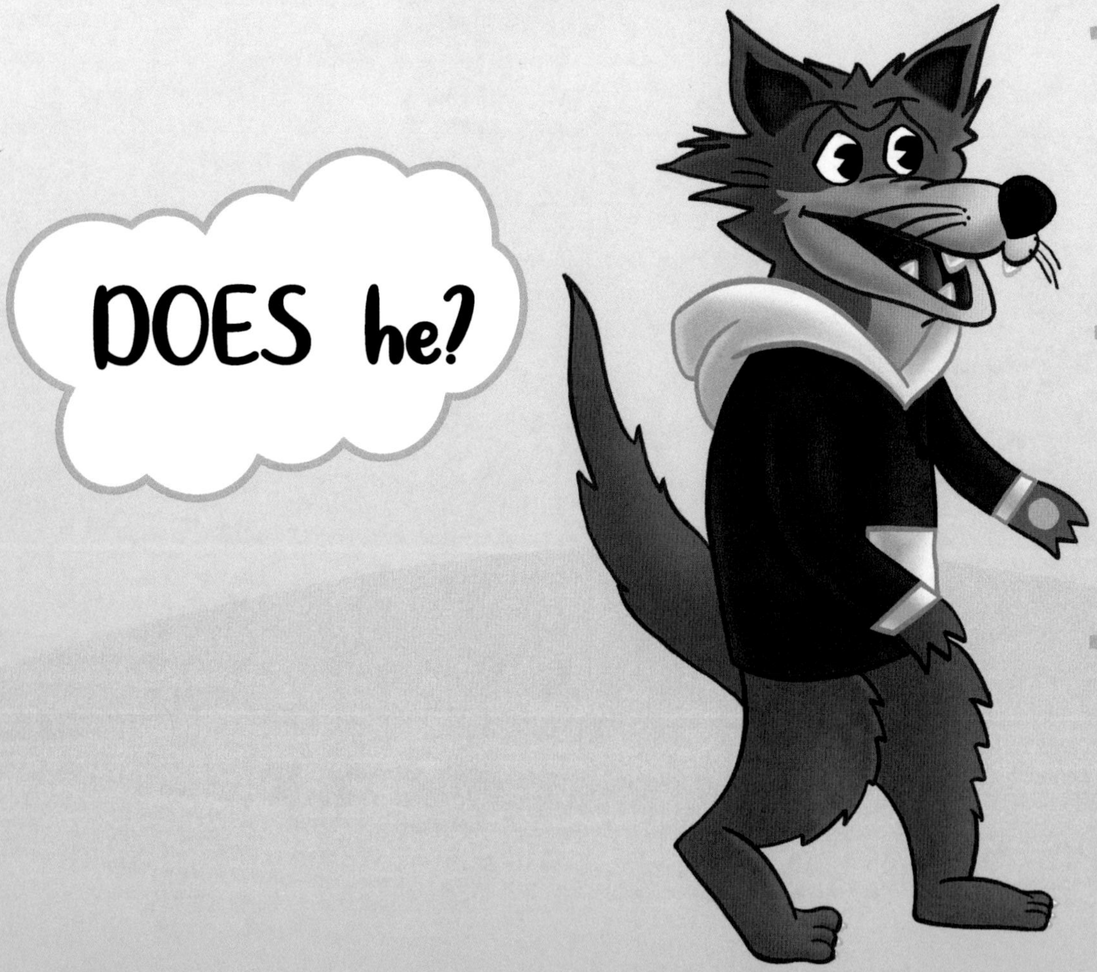

A. Blow the house down

GO TO PAGE

24

B. Talk and Compromise

GO TO PAGE

26

C. Think about his Feeling

"scared"
"lonely"
and "sad"

GO TO PAGE

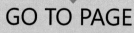

29

24 Blow the house down

The wolf huffs and puffs and tries to blow the house down.
He can not blow the house down, and now no one wants to play with him.
He walks away even more sad and alone.

"I didn't get my say, so I hope to find another way."

26 Talk and Compromise

The wolf looked sad. Creative Pig saw this and responded. "I am sorry, Mr. Wolf" said Creative Pig. "I see you are sad but my family needs me."

"But I am alone and need some help too," said Mr. Wolf. Creative Pig stopped. He took a deep breath and realized that in that moment, he felt afraid and sad too- just like the wolf.

The Creative Pig thought about what his brave brother would do, and decided to talk to the pig.
"I know it can be hard when you don't have any family, and you are alone and hungry" replied the pig.

The wolf softened his tone. "It is hard" voiced wolf. "Before I had my mom and dad. I got lost and I am trying to take care of myself".

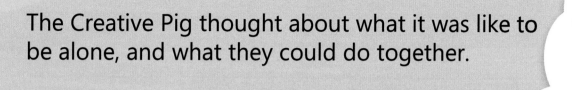

The Creative Pig thought about what it was like to be alone, and what they could do together.

"Why don't we work together," said the pig.
"You can gather wood for the houses and my brothers' and
I can share our food?".

Wolf smiled the biggest smile and jumped to
grab the wood.

The pig cooked a feast.
They all talked and worked together!
The wolf's heart and stomach finally felt happy and full.

THE END

 Think about his feelings.

Morning rose and Creative Pig came by the wolf-
who was deep in thought...

I want to
be happy

I want friends

I'm hurting
and lonely

I want to
belong

I yell and
hurt people

"**Hark!**" cried the wolf. "I have a better way!"
Bewildered, Creative Pig replied, " Pardon me,
what did you say?"

The wolf, with his eyes to the ground, sheepishly asked,
"Maybe you can **help** me. I am lonely and scared
and need some help"?

"Why of course!" said the pig. "Why didn't you ask?".
"I didn't know what to say," replied the wolf.
"Well, I am glad you did. **When you share your
emotions and use your words, I understand
you,**" replied the pig.

MR. WOLF FEELS

HAPPY
peaceful, content,
hopeful, proud,
inspired

MAD
angry, jealous,
hurt, insecure,
upset

SCARED
anxious, worthless,
fearful, nervous,
worried

SAD
lonley, bored,
quilty, unhappy,
powerless

31

"We understand you and forgive you" said the pigs. "Here is 5 dollars. You now have a new way. Keep doing the best you can" said Creative Pig. With that, the wolf did just that. With awareness and feelings, he built his own house and his new friends came to eat and play.

THE END

Acknowledgements

I would like to dedicate this to my parents. From a very young age, they modeled what it meant to be hard-working, determined and to live with heart. They came in the United States in hopes of building a better life for themselves and their children, and encouraged me to follow my dreams. They believed in both my abilities as a student, as a writer, and as a person, and it is for that reason I am writing this today.

I would like to thank my brother David, and my dad Lucien. I look up to my brother and I'm constantly inspired by his intelligence, his relentless dedication to his family and his ability to find the good in all people. To this day, my dad still surprises me, and I am inspired by his perseverance, loyalty, and determination-even when things seem insurmountable. I continue to strive for more and strive for better, with my brother sense of wonder my heart and my dad's love of to do list in my notepad.

I would also like to acknowledge my niece and nephew, Elia and Xavier. Their child like wonder and genuine honesty about the world inspires and fuels my heart. Thank you to both Michele and David for the thoughtfulness in how you interact with them, and for raising curious children who lead with their heart.

I would like to think my incredibly supportive friends who have been by my side. I'm grateful to have such kind, talented, strong, funny and intelligent people in my life. Thank you all for the inspiring questions, beta testing, feedback, google docs and wonderful support. You all inspire me with your strength, creativity, wisdom, and hearts.

I would like to thank every educator, teacher, supervisor and mentor who has stood by me and guided me along the way. Your continued dedication to teaching is motivating and because of you that I have a passion to pursue my dreams.

I would like to thank my team-April Cox, Pardeep and Priyam Mehra from PencilMasters and Lisa Caprelli. I am grateful for all of your guidance and support.

I especially want to dedicate this to my mom, Eleonor. She showed me what true strength, perseverance, and quiet but unwavering confidence really is. I am so proud of her and I miss her deeply every day. I will continue to live my life with her shining through me and will never stop trying to make her proud. I dedicate this book to her. Her love of the written word and artistic expression is expressed in every part of this book.

Every word, character and color placement contains my values, heart and soul.

Here's to you Momma, and to not giving up and not giving in and pursuing your deepest desires and dreams.

Author Bio

Dr. Stacey Zlotnick's love of books began at an early age. She spent hours sitting on the floor of her family's library room searching through Childcraft: The How and Why Encyclopedia, asking endless questions and watching her mom get lost in the romanticized and descriptive world of Pride and Prejudice. It was at this time that Dr. Stacey began a love affair with the written word not only for its artistic beauty, but for its connection. The words allowed her to transcend time, culture and space and experience life in the mind of another being. Each word fueled her fascination with people and how they think.

Dr. Stacey's natural interest in people, combined with her desire to help others, led her to the field of psychology.

Photo credit: photography: Ann Landstrom and Hair and make-up Andrea Bernal

Dr. Stacey Zlotnick is a doctor of clinical psychology, podcast host, author, spiritual leader and speaker. She completed her doctoral training at Stanford University School of Medicine, Pacific Graduate School of Psychology, and has had the privilege of training in a variety of clinical settings- including Oakland Children's Hospital, VA Palo Alto Health Care System, and Sharp Mesa Vista HealthCare System. She is grateful to have been mentored by some of the leading psychologists and psychiatrists in the field.

Her schooling brought her to San Diego where she matched for internship and stayed ever since. Professionally, she holds the role of Clinical Director at a private facility in San Diego and personally, she resides near the beach and writes often in her writing corner- with the Pacific Ocean waves in the background and her cat London, nearby.

Dr. Stacey is a self described forever-student and she believes it's important to inspire children to be curious, self-aware critical thinkers. She believes that it is important that children begin asking questions about themselves, the world and the people in it at an early age. She believes in empowering others through education. Dr. Stacey believes that kindness, empathy and compassion and a thirst for knowledge are the most powerful things that we can teach our children.

Mr. Rogers said, "One of the greatest dignities of humankind is that each successive generation is invested in the welfare of each new generation." And the first book of the 'Two-Sided Tails' series is her doing just that- in an empathic, honest, nurturing, engaging and fun way.

To learn more and connect with Dr. Stacey Zlotnick visit her at

 drstacey

drstaceyzlotnick@gmail.com

Made in the USA
San Bernardino, CA
26 February 2020